Share It! 1

Sharebook

Nicholas Beare

macmillan education

Table of Contents

Unit 5 **My Pets** pages 27–32	**Lesson 2** Student (A) page 27 Student (B) page 27	**Who Am I?**	Student A: *I have a bird. I don't have a cat.* Student B: *You're Tom.*
	Lesson 5 Student (A) page 29 Student (B) page 31	**Go Fish!**	Student A: *Do you have a big spider?* Student B: *No, I don't. Go fish!*
Unit 6 **At the Fair** pages 33–36	**Lesson 2** Student (A) page 33 Student (B) page 33	**Guess the Robot**	Student A: *It has three heads.* Student B: *Is it Robot 2?*
	Lesson 5 Student (A) page 35 Student (B) page 35	**Three Questions**	Student A: *Does it have big ears?* Student B: *Yes, it does.*
Unit 7 **At the Park** pages 37–40	**Lesson 2** Student (A) page 37 Student (B) page 38	**Find Five Differences**	Student A: *There are seven flowers next to the table.* Student B: *There are nine flowers next to the table.*
	Lesson 5 Student (A) page 39 Student (B) page 40	**Animal Lake**	Student A: *How many birds are there?* Student B: *There are twenty.*
Unit 8 **A Picnic** pages 41–46	**Lesson 2** Student (A) page 41 Student (B) page 43	**I Like It!**	Student A: *I like pizza.* Student B: *I don't like cheese.*
	Lesson 5 Student (A) page 45 Student (B) page 45	**The Food Quiz**	Student A: *Do you like candy?* Student B: *Yes, I do.*

Key Terms

Student A  Student B

cards

a page

face down

face up

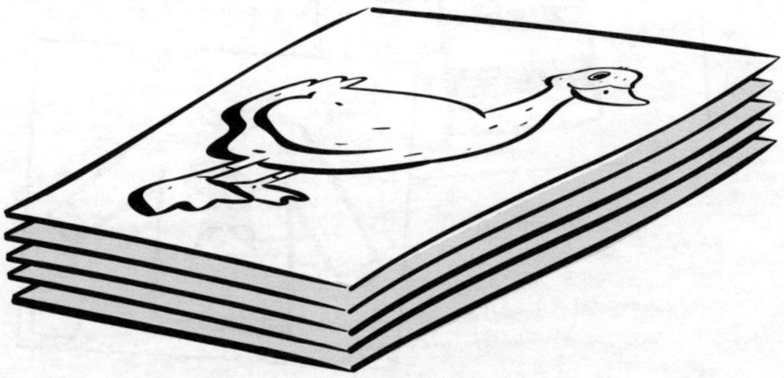

a pile of cards

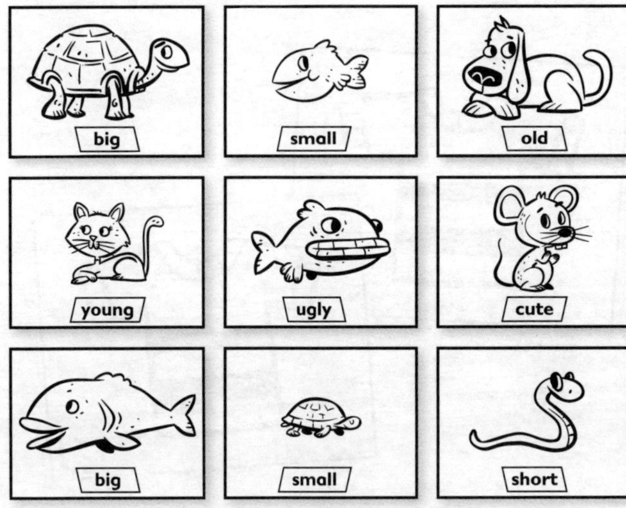

a set of cards

cut the cards

take a card

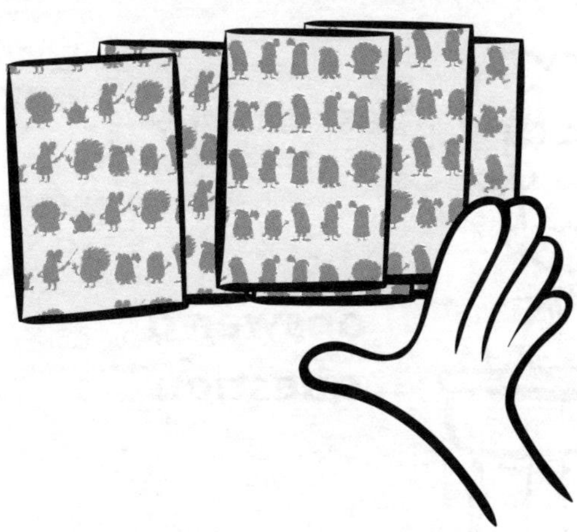

mix the cards

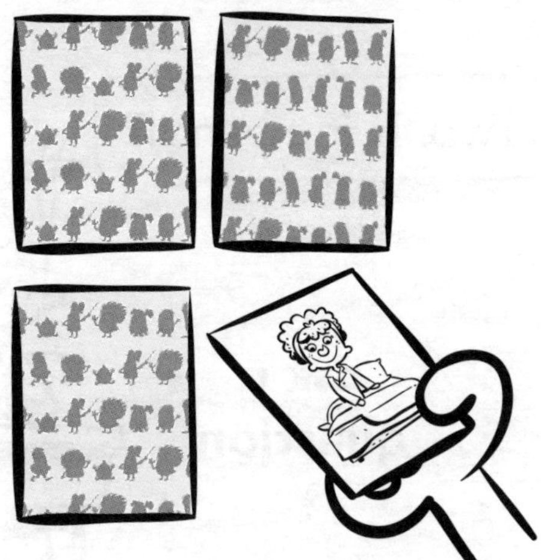

turn over a card

same

different

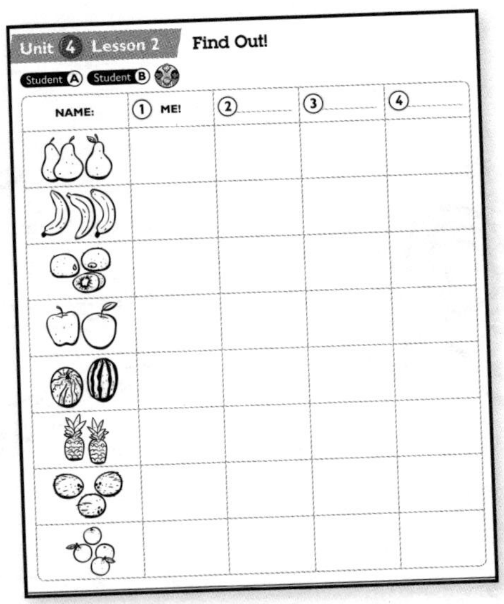

a chart

ask a question

answer a question

Unit 1 Lesson 2 What's This?

Student A

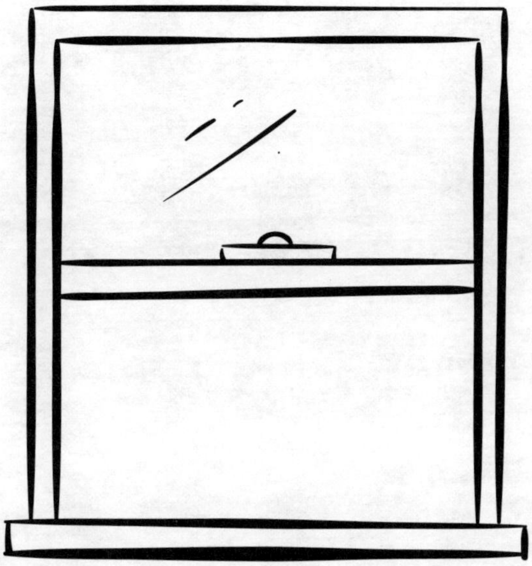

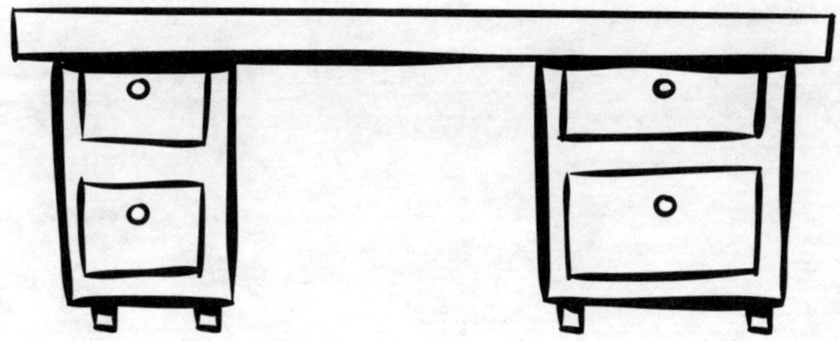

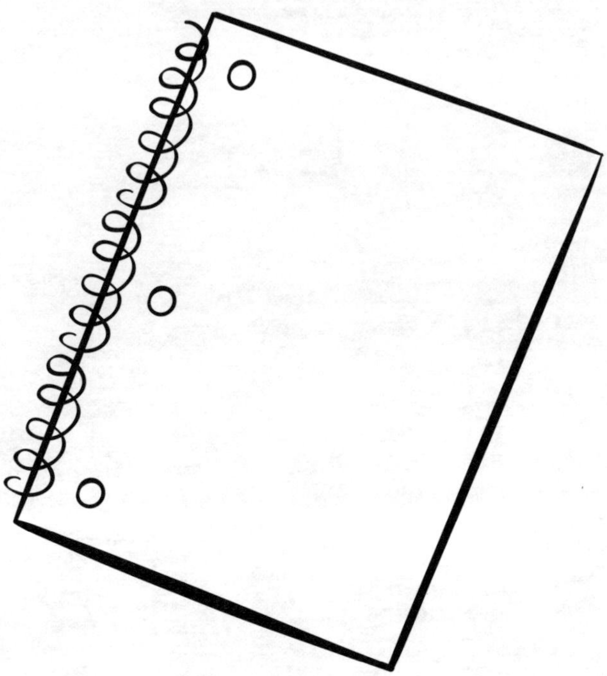

How to Play:
Students A and B: Color your cards.
Put all eight cards face up.
Study the cards. Then turn them face down.
Student A: Point to a card and ask.
Student B: Answer. Then turn the card over. You win the card if you are correct.

Example:
Student A: *What's this?*
Student B: *It's a red notebook.*

Unit 1 Lesson 2

What's This?

Student B

How to Play:
Students A and B: Color your cards.
Put all eight cards face up.
Study the cards. Then turn them face down.
Student A: Point to a card and ask.
Student B: Answer. Then turn the card over. You win the card if you are correct.

Example:
Student A: *What's this?*
Student B: *It's a red notebook.*

Unit 1 Lesson 5 Guess and Draw

Student A

1 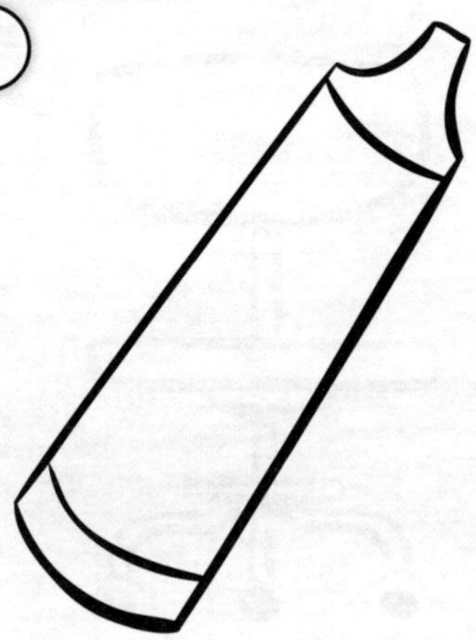	2 ?	3 ?
4 	5 	6 ?
7 ?	8 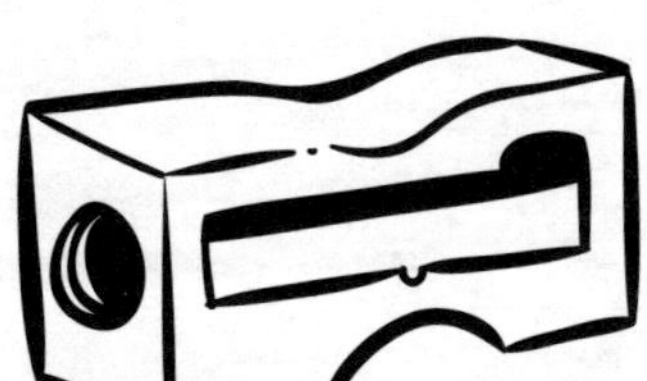	9 ?

How to Play:
Student A: Choose an empty box. Say the number and guess the item.
Student B: Listen, look at the picture, and answer.
Student A: Draw the item in the box.
Students A and B: You can ask two questions per turn. Then check your pictures. Are they the same?

Example:
Student A: *Number two. Is it a pencil?*
Student B: *No, it isn't.*
Student A: *Is it a ruler?*
Student B: *Yes, it is! Draw it!*

Unit 1 Lesson 5 Guess and Draw

Student B

1 ?	2 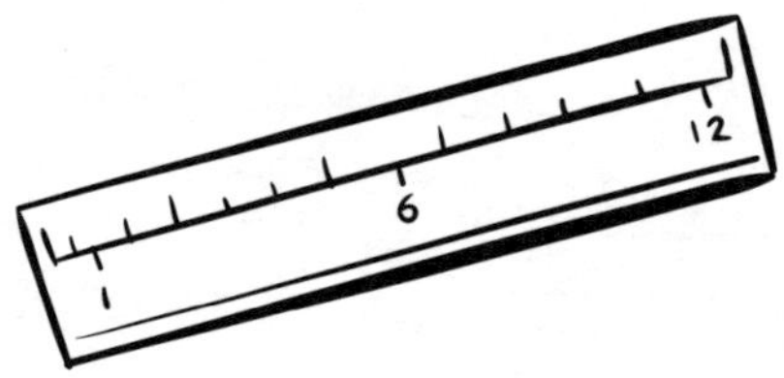	3 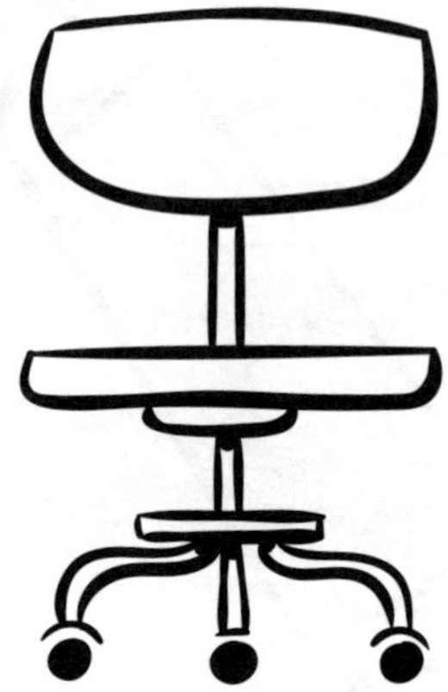
4 ?	5 ?	6 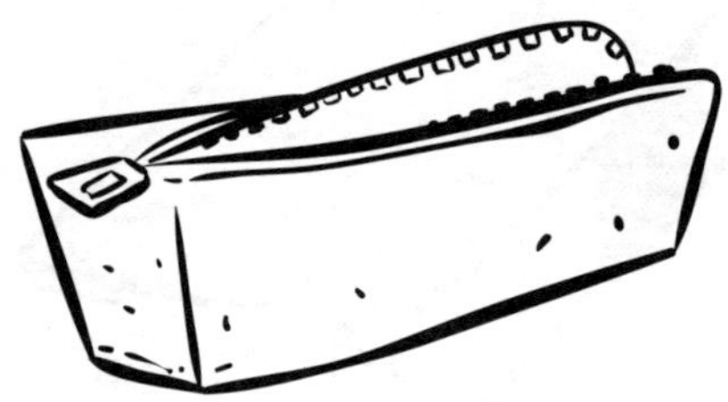
7 	8 ?	9 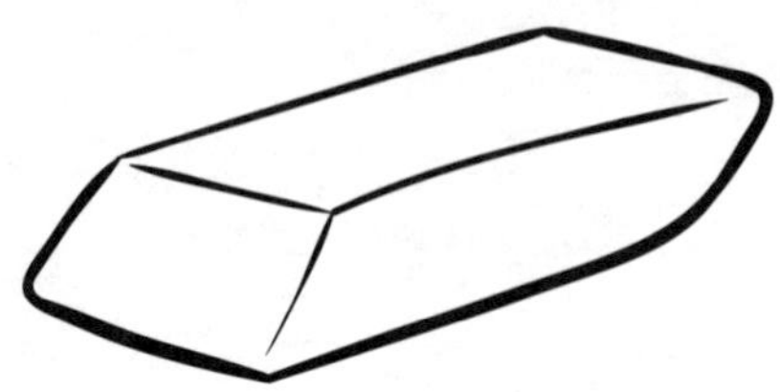

How to Play:
Student A: Choose an empty box. Say the number and guess the item.
Student B: Listen, look at the picture, and answer.
Student A: Draw the item in the box.
Students A and B: You can ask two questions per turn. Then check your pictures. Are they the same?

Example:
Student A: *Number two. Is it a pencil?*
Student B: *No, it isn't.*
Student A: *Is it a ruler?*
Student B: *Yes, it is! Draw it!*

Unit 2 Lesson 2 Family Pictures

Student A Student B

How to Play:
Students A and B: Draw pictures of your friends or family members.
Show your pictures to your partner.
Student B: Point to a picture and ask.
Student A: Answer. Then share your pictures with others.

Example:
Student A: *Who's this?*
Student B: *This is my sister.*

How Many Toys?

Student A

1	________	________	trucks	5 one purple robot
2	________	________	cars	6 two pink dolls
3	________	________	bikes	7 three yellow kites
4	________	________	balls	8 five brown books

How to Play:
Students A and B: Ask your partner about the toys on their list. Write the missing numbers and colors in your list. Then draw and color the toys in your picture. Check your pictures, are they the same?

Example:
Student A: *How many trucks?*
Student B: *Three trucks.*
Student A: *What color are they?*
Student B: *They're orange.*

Unit 2 Lesson 5

How Many Toys?

Student B

1 three orange trucks

2 four green cars

3 two red bikes

4 five blue balls

5 ____________ ____________ robot

6 ____________ ____________ dolls

7 ____________ ____________ kites

8 ____________ ____________ books

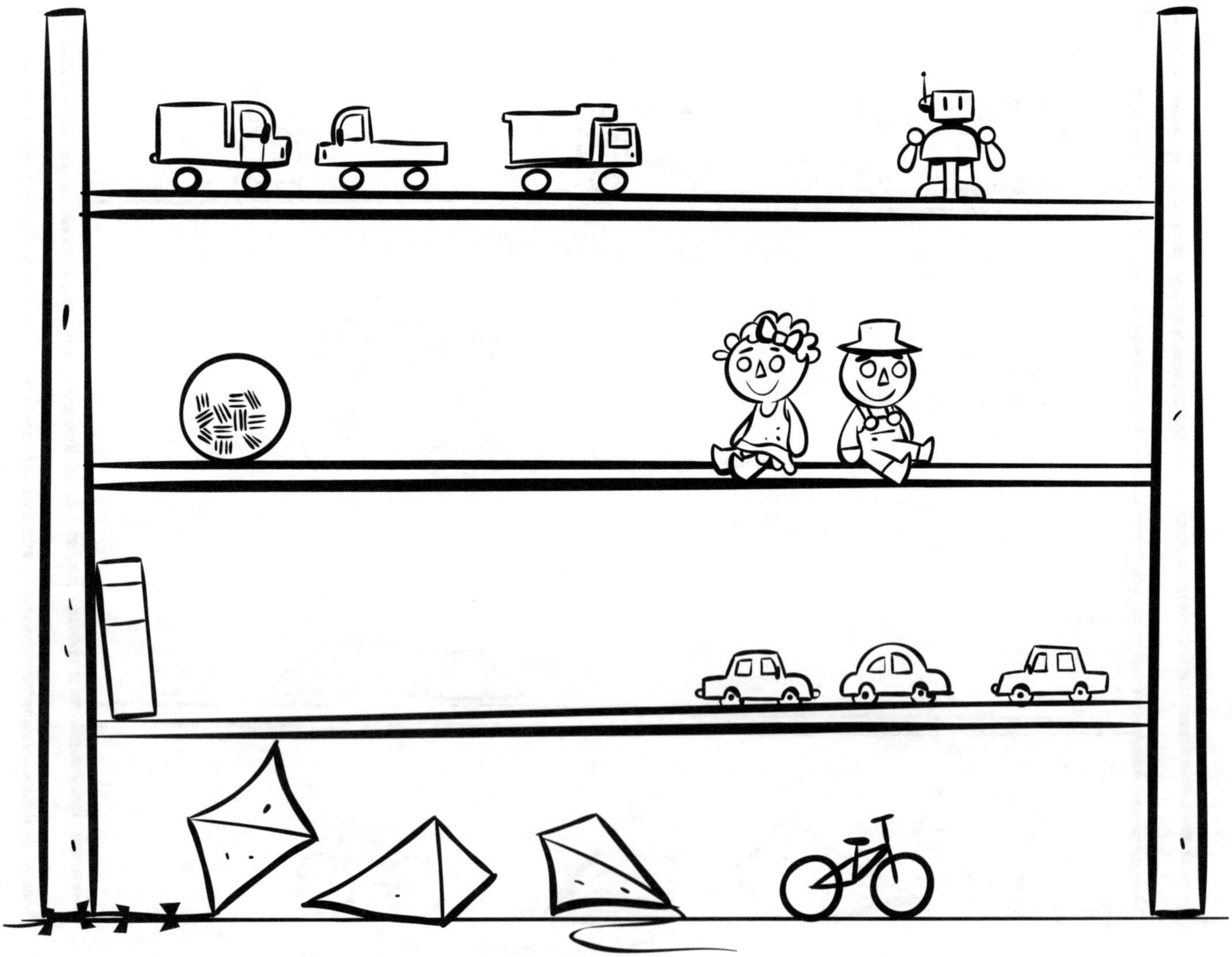

How to Play:
Students A and B: Ask your partner about the toys on their list. Write the missing numbers and colors in your list. Then draw and color the toys in your picture. Check your pictures, are they the same?

Example:
Student A: *How many trucks?*
Student B: *Three trucks.*
Student A: *What color are they?*
Student B: *They're orange.*

Unit 3 Lesson 2 Find Four Differences

Student A

1

2

3

4

5

6

How to Play:

Students A and B: Talk to find four differences between pages 17 and 18.

Students A and B: Fill in the boxes. ✔ same ✘ different

Example:

Student A: *Number one. She's a cook.*

Student B: *She isn't a cook. She's a vet.*

Students A and B: *Oh, that's different!*

1. ✘

Find Four Differences

Student B

1

2

3

4

5

6

How to Play:
Students A and B: Talk to find four differences between pages 17 and 18.
Students A and B: Fill in the boxes. ✔ same ✘ different

Example:
Student A: *Number one. She's a cook.*
Student B: *She isn't a cook. She's a vet.*
Students A and B: *Oh, that's different!*
1. ✘

Unit 3 Lesson 5 Guess the Job

Student A

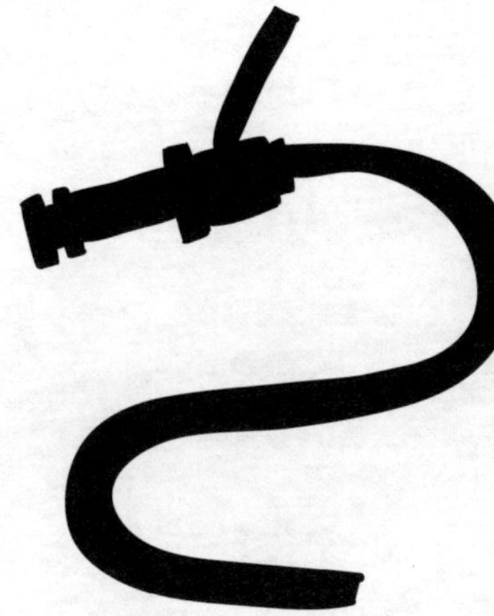

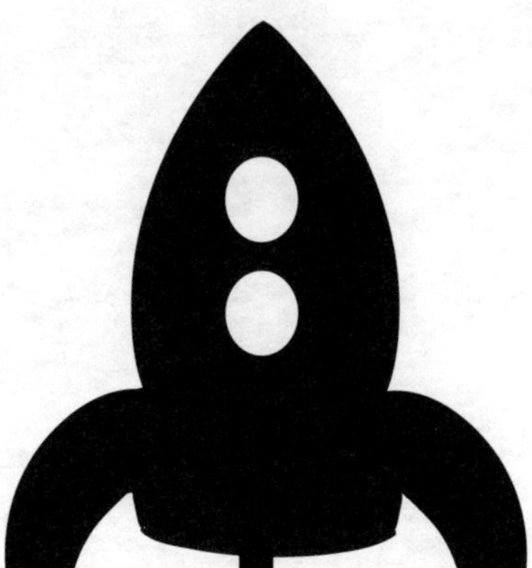
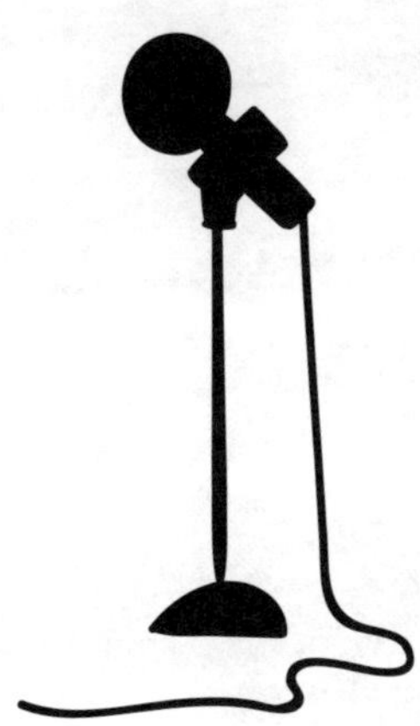

How to Play:
Students A and B: Put 14 job cards face down. Put four he/she cards face up.
Student A: Point to a he/she card and say *he* or *she*.
Student B: Take a job card. Don't show it!
Student A: Guess the job to win the card (three guesses per card).

Example:
Student A: *She!* (points to a she card)
Student B: *OK!* (takes a job card)
Student A: *Is she a vet?* Student B: *No, she isn't.*
Student A: *Is she a pilot?* Student B: *Yes, she is!*

Unit 3 Lesson 5

Guess the Job

Student B

he

she

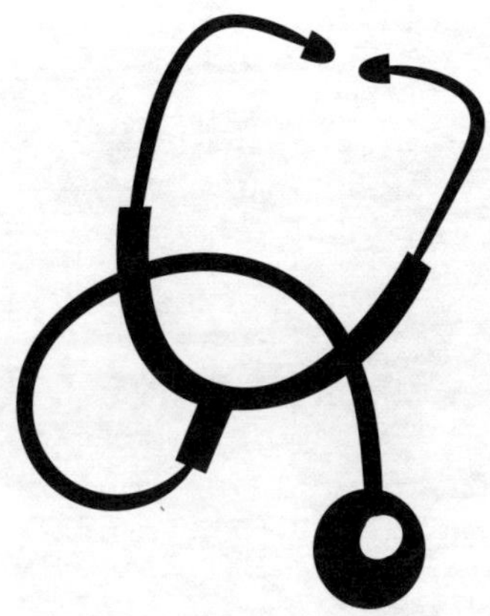

How to Play:

Students A and B: Put 14 job cards face down. Put four he/she cards face up.
Student A: Point to a he/she card and say *he* or *she*.
Student B: Take a job card. Don't show it!
Student A: Guess the job to win the card (three guesses per card).

Example:

Student A: *She!* (points to a she card)
Student B: *OK!* (takes a job card)
Student A: *Is she a vet?* Student B: *No, she isn't.*
Student A: *Is she a pilot?* Student B: *Yes, she is!*

Unit 4 Lesson 2 Find Your Friends!

Student A **Find Lucy, Kim, Sue, and Alice.**

How to Play:
Students A and B: Ask and answer about the people in the house.
Student A: Find the people and write their names.
Check your answers with your partner.

Example:
Student A: *Where's Sue?*
Student B: *She's in the yard.*

Unit 4 Lesson 2

Find Your Friends!

Student B

Find Ben, Matt, Mark, and Pat.

How to Play:
Students A and B: Ask and answer about the people in the house.
Student B: Find the people and write their names.
Check your answers with your partner.

Example:
Student A: *Where's Sue?*
Student B: *She's in the yard.*

Unit 4 Lesson 5 Find the Differences

Student A

	Same	Different
crayons	☐	☐
backpack	☐	☐
ball	☐	☐
kites	☐	☐
robots	☐	☐
books	☐	☐

How to Play:

Students A and B: Look at the items in each room.
Students A and B: Talk to find four differences between the two rooms.
Students A and B: Are your pictures the same or different? Check.

Example:

Student A: *Where are the kites?*
Student B: *They're under the table.*
Student A: *That's the same.*

Find the Differences

Student B

	Same	Different
crayons	☐	☐
backpack	☐	☐
ball	☐	☐
kites	☐	☐
robots	☐	☐
books	☐	☐

How to Play:
Students A and B: Look at the items in each room.
Students A and B: Talk to find four differences between the two rooms.
Students A and B: Are your pictures the same or different? Check.

Example:
Student A: *Where are the kites?*
Student B: *They're under the table.*
Student A: *That's the same.*

Unit 5 Lesson 2 Who Am I?

Student A Student B

How to Play:
Students A and B: Look at the page.
Student A: Choose a boy or girl and make sentences about their pets.
Student B: Look and say who it is. Write a check next to the name.
Take turns until you finish.

Example:
Student A: *I have a bird. I don't have a cat.*
Student B: *You're Tom.*
Student A: *Yes.*

Go Fish!

Student A

big

small

old

young

ugly

cute

big

small

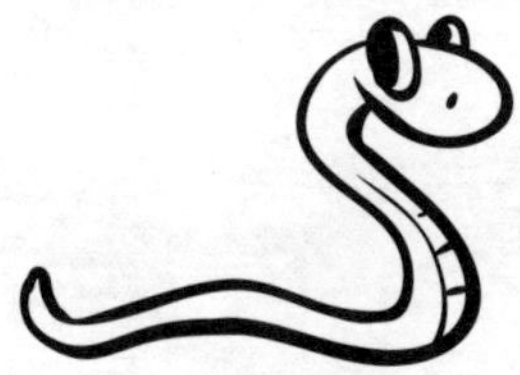

short

long

ugly

cute

How to Play:

Students A and B: Mix the cards. Put them face down in a pile. Take three cards each.
Student A: Ask Student B for a card. Try to make a pair.
Student B: Give the card to Student A, or say *Go fish!*
Student A: Take Student B's card, or take a card from the pile.
Student A: Put any pairs face up in front of you.

Example:

Student A: *Do you have a small mouse?*
Student B: *Yes, I do. Here you go.*
Student B: *Do you have a big spider?*
Student A: *No, I don't. Go fish!*

Unit 5 Lesson 5 Go Fish!

Student B

big

small

old

young

ugly

cute

big

small

short

long

ugly

cute

How to Play:

Students A and B: Mix the cards. Put them face down in a pile. Take three cards each.
Student A: Ask Student B for a card. Try to make a pair.
Student B: Give the card to Student A, or say *Go fish*!
Student A: Take Student B's card, or take a card from the pile.
Student A: Put any pairs face up in front of you.

Example:

Student A: *Do you have a small mouse?*
Student B: *Yes, I do. Here you go.*
Student B: *Do you have a big spider?*
Student A: *No, I don't. Go fish!*

Unit 6 Lesson 2 Guess the Robot

Student A Student B

Robot Cards

Robot 1

Robot 2

Robot 3

Robot 4

Robot 5

Robot 6

Robot 7

Robot 8

Robot 9

How to Play:
Students A and B each have a set of cards.
Student A: Put your robot cards in a pile, face down.
Student B: Spread your robot cards face up.
Student A: Turn over a card from the pile and describe the robot.
Student B: Try to guess the robot.
Students A and B: Take turns turning over cards and guessing the robot.

Example:
Student A: *It has three heads.*
Student B: *Is it Robot 2?*
Student A: *Yes, good job!*

Three Questions

Student A Student B

How to Play:
Student A: Look and choose one of the animals on the shelf.
Student B: Ask Student A about the face of the animal.
Student A: Look and answer Student B.
Student B: Guess the animal or ask again. You can ask three questions. Check the box if you guess correctly.
Students A and B: Take turns. Continue until all the animals are checked.

Example:
Student B: *Does it have big ears?*
Student A: *Yes, it does.*
Student B: *Does it have a small nose?*
Student A: *No, it doesn't.*
Student B: *Is it the cat?*
Student A: *No, it isn't.*

Unit 7 Lesson 2

Find Five Differences

Student A

How to Play:
Student A: Choose an object in your picture and talk about it.
Student B: Talk about the same object in your picture.
Students A and B: Find five differences. Circle the differences.

Example:
Student A: *There's a slide.*
Student B: *There's a slide.*
Student A: *There are seven flowers next to the table.*
Student B: *There are nine flowers next to the table.*
Students A and B: *That's different.*

Unit 7 Lesson 2 Find Five Differences

Student B

How to Play:
Student A: Choose an object in your picture and talk about it.
Student B: Talk about the same object in your picture.
Students A and B: Find five differences. Circle the differences.

Example:
Student A: *There's a slide.*
Student B: *There's a slide.*
Student A: *There are seven flowers next to the table.*
Student B: *There are nine flowers next to the table.*
Students A and B: *That's different.*

Unit 7 Lesson 5 Animal Lake

Student A

	Same	Different
birds	☐	☐
turtles	☐	☐
cats	☐	☐
snakes	☐	☐

	Same	Different
fish	☐	☐
spiders	☐	☐
dogs	☐	☐
mice	☐	☐

How to Play:
Student A: Ask Student B about the animals in their picture. Use the language "*How many* _____ *are there?*"
Student B: Tell Student A how many there are.
Students A and B: Is the number the same or different? Check.

Example:
Student A: *How many birds are there?*
Student B: *There are twenty.*
Student A: *That's different. Your turn!*

Unit 7 Lesson 5 Animal Lake

Student B

	Same	Different
birds	☐	☐
turtles	☐	☐
cats	☐	☐
snakes	☐	☐

	Same	Different
fish	☐	☐
spiders	☐	☐
dogs	☐	☐
mice	☐	☐

How to Play:
Student A: Ask Student B about the animals in their picture. Use the language "*How many* ____ *are there?*"
Student B: Tell Student A how many there are.
Students A and B: Is the number the same or different? Check.

Example:
Student A: *How many birds are there?*
Student B: *There are twenty.*
Student A: *That's different. Your turn!*

Unit 8 Lesson 2 I Like It!

Student A

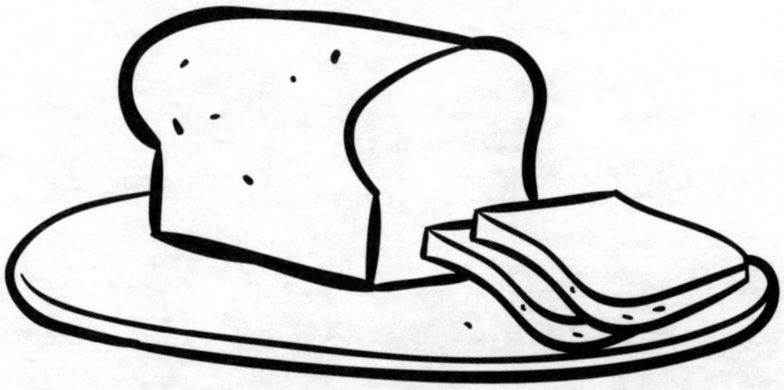

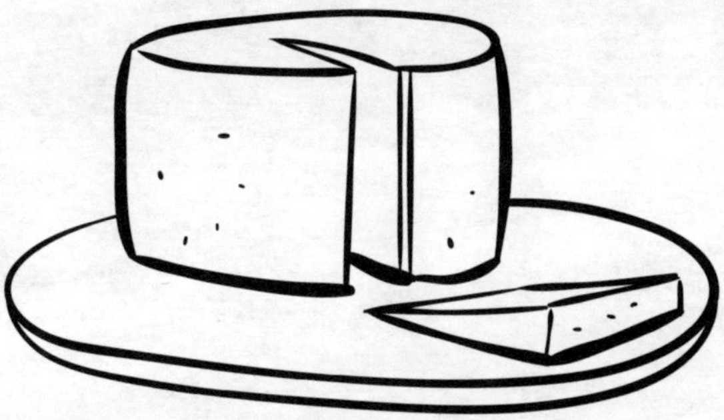

like

like

don’t like

don’t like

How to Play:
Students A and B: Mix the cards and put them face down.
Student A: Turn over two cards. If you turn over a word card and a picture card, make a sentence and take the cards.
Student B: Take a turn.
Students A and B: Play until you use all the cards.

Example:
Student A: *I like pizza.*
Student B: *I don’t like cheese.*

Unit 8 Lesson 2 I Like It!

Student B

like

like

don't like

don't like

How to Play:
Students A and B: Mix the cards and put them face down.
Student A: Turn over two cards. If you turn over a word card and a picture card, make a sentence and take the cards.
Student B: Take a turn.
Students A and B: Play until you use all the cards.

Example:
Student A: *I like pizza.*
Student B: *I don't like cheese.*

Unit 8 Lesson 5 The Food Quiz

Student A Student B

Do you like ...?

	**yes** (2 points)	**no** (0 points)
	**yes** (0 points)	**no** (2 points)
	**yes** (3 points)	**no** (0 points)
	**yes** (2 points)	**no** (1 point)
	**yes** (1 point)	**no** (1 point)
	**yes** (0 points)	**no** (2 points)
	**yes** (2 points)	**no** (1 point)
	**yes** (1 point)	**no** (1 point)
	**yes** (3 points)	**no** (0 points)
	**yes** (0 points)	**no** (2 points)

Name ______________________

Score ______________________

Points
1–10 Unhealthy
11–15 Healthy
16–20 Very Healthy

How to Play:
Student A: Ask Student B about the food.
Student B: Answer the questions.
Student A: Circle Student B's answers on your page. Add up the points and tell Student B their score. Then change roles.

Example:
Student A: *Do you like candy?*
Student B: *Yes, I do.*

My Sharebook Game Log

Sharebook 1		Game	Date	Players
1	Lesson 2	What's This?		
	Lesson 5	Guess and Draw		
2	Lesson 2	Family Pictures		
	Lesson 5	How Many Toys?		
3	Lesson 2	Find Four Differences		
	Lesson 5	Guess the Job		
4	Lesson 2	Find Your Friends!		
	Lesson 5	Find the Differences		
5	Lesson 2	Who Am I?		
	Lesson 5	Go Fish!		
6	Lesson 2	Guess the Robot		
	Lesson 5	Three Questions		
7	Lesson 2	Find Five Differences		
	Lesson 5	Animal Lake		
8	Lesson 2	I Like It!		
	Lesson 5	The Food Quiz		

I can play games in English!

Macmillan Education Limited
4 Crinan Street
London N1 9XW

Companies and representatives throughout the world

Sharebook ISBN 978-1-380-02276-9
Student Book Pack ISBN 978-1-380-02272-1

Written by Nicholas Beare

The author has asserted their right to be identified as the author of this work in accordance with the Copyright, Designs and Patents Act 1988.

Share It! is a registered trademark published by Macmillan Education Limited

First published 2020

Designed by Pronk Media, Inc.
Illustrated by Drew Pocza pp. 4, 5, 6, 7, 9, 11, 12, 13, 15, 16, 17, 18, 19, 21, 23, 24, 25, 26, 27, 29, 31, 33, 35, 37, 38, 39, 40, 41, 43, 45; Emi Ordás & Wedoo Studio p. 47.
Cover design by Roberto Martinez, Marcin Rojek, and Wojciech Szulik
Cover illustration by Emi Ordás

Author's acknowledgements
The author would like to thank the *Share It!* team for their support and encouragement.

Printed and bound in Brazil.
2025
75